HOW TO TRAIN YOUR HUMAN:

THE DOG'S GUIDE

A. J. Brenchley

HALFNIGHT BOOKS

ISBN: 098868392X

ISBN-13: 978-0-9886839-2-1

Dedication

To Chris: The Claw

and

To Chummy: The Fang

When the Claw meets the Fang,
it only ends in kisses.

HOW TO TRAIN YOUR HUMAN

CONTENTS

HOW TO TRAIN YOUR HUMAN

Woof-Woof (or: the introduction)

Let's face it: you're having a wonderful time. Ever since your Uncle Urk, several thousand times removed, decided to befriend Flint (the male human) and Oofy (his lady love), a dog's life has been...a dog's life. You have the best of everything: shelter from weather, a place on the rug, and the protection of the world's Biggest Cheese. Not to mention that humans are the only beings in the universe to have discovered a) feather pillows and b) the pepperoni and anchovy pizza. If only *opossums* had had the sense to make themselves Man's Best Friend. Or aardvarks. But they didn't, so they've been left behind. Your own standard of living, over thousands of years with humankind, has progressed from somewhat fine to totally terrific.

Materially, you know what I mean. Your coat is lush and free of fleas, and even your breath is sweet: vultures don't soar overhead when you pant, now that mint-chews and toothpaste are a habit. You get coats in winter and rides in cars – and we're not talking chariots, baby.

On the other hand, your freedom is in tatters. When did humans start outfoxing you so often instead of the other way around?

I'm sure you've noticed. Humans of the 21st century have all sorts of newfangled, fancy ideas about how to live with dogs. They read books, take lessons, and watch TV programs, all in an effort to learn about *you*. But let's not be Pollyannas here: they are also seeking clever new ways to boss you around more effectively. And when you don't comply, or you indulge in minor doggy hijinks, they whip out the dog-brain manual or the training handbook, or phone their smarty-pants friends for advice. Very often they bamboozle you with new techniques they've learned, foiling your unauthorized plans. This situation is clearly unsustainable. Every dog must be a bit unauthorized in order to be happy.

And yet, this is not even the whole story. For while the great bell-jar of human knowledge has been smothering your air of mystery, certain aspects of your nature have also been downplayed or misunderstood. Perhaps you are scolded for barking at the door, even though a man with a shoulder bag and envelopes tries every day to break in (at about the same time, except on Sundays). Since when was a flower-seed catalogue an Open Sesame to your home? And then there are the humans that make you fill in for somebody else, so you're treated like a cat with slobber or a hypercarnivorous canary. Even worse is when humans think you're some sort of plush toy, the difference being the flea prevention and the fact that you need taking out.

So despite the benefits, it's not easy being a dog of the postmodern age, in the Holocene epoch of the Cenozoic Era (of the Phanerozoic Eon, since we're showing off). When it comes to having their own way, humans make the most of what they've learned about your secrets. Yet — and this is important — when it comes to your own deeper longings, you remain as much a mystery as ever.

You are caught between the devil of human know-it-allness and the deep blue sea of their cluelessness.

Many dogs have no real complaints, of course. Their worst problems are biscuits with cranberry flavour and the fact that Daddy snores in bed. Humans are a highly varied bunch, and some are more controlling or more dopey than others. In this book we'll have a look at different types of *Homo sapiens*, and suggest condign strategies for dealing with them. Even if you are generally happy with your humans, you still might want to expand your personal bag of tricks – those ruses, workarounds, and clever little ploys that allow you to have more of your own way.

The time has come to reassess the life you are living, and ask whether you're getting enough out of it. It is *your* job to maintain the human-dog relationship *as it was meant to be*, and this guide will show you how. You, too, can train your humans, and give them a better life as a result. With a little devious plotting and some judicious, harmless sabotage, you will very soon be happier — and the people you live with will be *glad* to see the brighter-eyed, swishier-tailed you.

This guide cannot change the fact of human curiosity, which after all is not completely diabolical (some of your food was devised in labs that also make dinners for astronauts, and every molecule must be good and tasty or the astronauts would quickly go bonkers). What it *can* do is help you to achieve the rightful balance of power, to restore the yin of what you want against the yang of how humans see things.

In a moment, we'll discuss goals and tactics. But first, let's take a closer look at the main animal in your life: the human being.

Are these dancers' arm cuffs or napkin rings? No, they're antique dog collars, a few centuries old. They may look posh, but imagine your neck in one of these. Life has been better for dogs and their humans since stiff and metallic forms of attire (mail and plate armour, starched ruffs, corsets) gave way to soft cotton, nubbly wool, and floppy nylon.

Image is courtesy of The Dog Collar Museum, The Leeds Castle Foundation, Kent, England

This dog is *not* wearing a napkin ring or the "necklace" of a leash, yet appears to be having the time of his life. At one with his environment, the dog sails like the clouds, flows like the sea, and changes like the strand – even sharing the colours of them all.

It's lovely to be free when you know that someone loves you. That's the balance we all seek: the "freedom to be me" and the comfort and pleasure of sharing with somebody else.

1.

The Human Animal:
Why do they do what they do?

I'll shock no one by announcing that humans have a very high opinion of themselves. On the whole, they are inclined to assess themselves as brainy, accomplished, good at hairstyles and barbecuing, and nothing short of magnificent. And it's very important that *you*, as the dog in their lives, help to support this self-perception – rather than seeing them as funny-looking apes without the clean lines of fallow deer, the beauty of horses, the power of leopard seals, or the self-showering capacities of elephants. As semi-furred monkey-cousins with ridiculous ears and weirdo things like glasses, phones, and accordions hanging off them, humans are the visual laughing-stock of the world organic community. *You* do an admirable job of ignoring that. Most humans assume that you don't notice their failings, and can't tell the difference between wrap-around sunglasses and bare eyes you can actually look into. Of *course* you can tell, but dogs are naturally the most tactful creatures on Earth, and you're much more interested in what Grumpy-This-Morning has got for breakfast, anyway.

I've already mentioned "laughingstock". Did you know that the human being is the only risible animal? I don't mean they are the only creature that deserves to be laughed at, though you might be excused for thinking so at times. Humans are the only creatures that laugh. They are the only animal whose sense of the funny is so strong and acute that they have to do that strange breathy vocalizing known as "guffawing" – an odd word for a *very* odd behaviour. They are the only creatures in the history of Earth (age: 4.5 billion years or so) to titter, snort, chuckle, cackle, giggle, chortle, and belly-laugh, often while tears run down their cheeks. Other animals die in all seriousness. Humans are the only ones that might possibly die laughing. Is this peculiar? You betcha. But not necessarily harmful to *you*, the canine companion. It must be the famous sense of humour that allows your people to chamois-gloss your hair, brush your teeth and clip your nails, feed you low-cal meals, and gallop you alongside their cruising bike, while *they* live as one of The Screen People, to be dug up by archaeologists a thousand years from now, bones intermingled with remotes, chair controls, and petrified popcorn.

But laughter isn't the only way that humans are distinctly mystifying. Their play time is limited by something called "work", though you can't imagine what this could be. Their amusements hardly strike you as amusing. (Singing in the shower; mowing weeds and calling it a "lawn"; setting off the fire alarm with burnt toast – again: what's it all about?) However, what humans actually *do* with their time is of little concern to you; the important thing is *how* they do it, and how that affects *you*. At the risk of oversimplifying, human behavior affects you at any given time in one of four basic ways. Whether they intend it or not, their behaviour is:

      a) comforting / cosy / affectionate / kind
      b) stimulating / interesting / fun
      c) dull, or
      e) disturbing.

It's not the *activity* you care about (which most of the time is a mystery anyway); it's the spirit in which it's done. People can be a bore while digging flower beds, but if they make very silly noises and let you nose around the soil, then that makes them *fun* while digging flower beds. You are willing to see the fun in almost anything, as long as your human is, too. But you never know whether they'll choose to be fun or whether they'll just be funereal. They seem capable of going either way.

What you have to realize is that, unlike dogs, humans are a mass of contradictions. Dogs are generally fond of smells, interested in dirt, willing to romp, and happy to devour things at any time of day. (Not necessarily food – but puppies soon learn.) Dogs, you might say, are principled and consistent.

Humans by contrast may like a certain kind of cheese, yet the same cheese with a drink the colour of bricks and the flavour of leather (or oak or blackcurrants), makes them turn up their noses. Go figure.

They are raucous animals, laughing at the tops of their lungs and blaring music as well as the vacuum cleaner, yet when you bark at similar decibels, they have a sudden need for quiet. As if your voice sounds worse than a leaf-blower motor!

Humans don't mind if you sniff their beginnings – heads, hands, and feet – but they want you to pretend that they don't have a middle, and especially, they don't have an end. "Nothing to sniff here, folks". Weird, when you consider that all odours are valid, if not uniformly informative. From your tolerant doggy perspective, getting in a huff about smells is like smiling at all the ice creams at the ice cream counter until the chocolate mint and orange sherbet, then announcing "that's it, I'm leaving!" and banging the door on the way out.

As for food and romping, humans manage to be uptight about these things, too – partly because of "work", as mentioned, and partly because of something called a "diet". And yet you could have sworn you smelled cake crumbs in the chair crack.... Principled and consistent? Forget it.

A random collection of human artifacts.

Being attuned to the fundamentals of life, these objects don't mean anything to you. But to your human, you can bet that each one in its own way is *tremendously* important. Especially the sunglasses. And the salt. And the car key. And the lipstick. And the phone....

We all know that humans can be impossible at times. They chatter a good deal, making your eyes glaze over. It's not just the repetition, though they do repeat themselves a lot. ("No" and "good dog" are el boresville, aren't they? Why can't they say it ভাল কুকুর in Bengali or *chó tốt* in Vietnamese?) What you really can't fathom is the breath they waste when they know you can't be listening. You look for need-to-know information, nothing more. For instance, no one needs to hear *all* of "That sausage is *not* for you! I don't know where it rolled to but I *don't* want you to eat it!" In that entire statement, only "sausage" is the least bit interesting. Like any normal, well-adjusted dog, you wouldn't waste time pondering the grammar, you'd be off to find the sausage.

Then there is the fact of human inscrutability. Let's say your human is lazy/arthritic/sore from exercising. They look up at you and say something disapproving. Then, three minutes later, which is the time it takes for them to get off the sofa/treadmill/chaise longue, they pick up the nearest Chinese menu and swat you with it on the rump. You, of course, are nonplussed. Was it the growling, scratching, nipping at a fly, or the chewing of houseplants they objected to? You will never know, three minutes being quite a long time in which to get into trouble. And anyway, as far as you're concerned, everything you did was totally above-board and perfectly in order.

What you need to do, as a dog, is focus on the human things that make them so endearing. Their generous love, for instance. The tender expression on their faces when the two of you must part, and they – looking through the car window – gaze at you – looking through the house window – misty-eyed. Their willingness to throw things, roll on the floor with you, and make monkey noises just to entertain you, even though this wins them no prestige with other humans. Their sense of being really your "mummy" or "daddy", even if officially they're "owners". The fact that however many people, cats, and terrapins they have around to cuddle, they never seem to tire of cuddling *you*.

If a sweet young human can be lifted up to spare her weary legs, why not you?

Nice to have mum and dad nearby, but not always humming at your shoulder like a flower-besotted hummingbird. Even if it's understandable.

These swans would be lovely to play with, if only mummy would allow it. You'd like to do your own version of "swan dive" but they won't let you in the water!

2.

What Kind Of Human Do You Have?

Problem people and strategies for dealing with them

Humans are masters at creating problems, which can often become the dog's problems, too. Even so, many dogs are blessed with sweetheart people who really try to make life enjoyable. If that's you, congratulations! If that's not you, then perhaps your human is one of various human types examined below. In each case, we describe the failings involved, and then suggest a strategy for dealing with them. If you recognize your human, here on the page in black and white, there is no reason for despondency. With patience and perseverance, most problems can be remedied somewhat, and sometimes they can even be corrected. Humans are willing and able to learn if you are loving, kind, and dogged in pursuit of your goal.

The Stodge

The Stodge is a responsible type that is deeply deficient in imagination. You are a *dog*, which means that you enjoy the exercise of particular faculties, such as seeing and hearing and biting, which you have in spades. But the Stodge might as well be a food-and-drink dispenser, and you might as well be a parrot. Though truth to tell, if you *were* a finch or parrot, the conversation between you might be more scintillating. Your human is not much of a talker, and there's never any squealing, whooping, giggling, or affectionate gibberish to liven things up a bit. When they do condescend to speak, they sound either like Jeeves the Butler or Jeeves the Butler's mother. The only thing you can hope for on the jolly-sounds front is the rare occasion when they fart.

If only!

The Stodge is very dutiful about walking you, without realizing just how grateful you are to be out where the smelly things are. Your exercise allotment is predictable, but unfortunately, so is the route. Your chief problem, of course, is boredom.

Everyone else knows that a pair of socks tied together make a terrific floppy propeller, but this would never occur to the Stodge. For this person, the only conceivable arrangement for socks is with one sock-top folded over the other, laid flat and grouped by colour in a drawer. Needless to say, this by-the-book thinking is just deadly for dogs. It means that any rawhide bone is simply handed over, and any treat, however thoughtfully chosen, is blandly presented to you. There is never any question of throwing treat-bits for you to chase on the patio, or hither and yon around rooms of the house. Nor are you ever shown two or three goodies at a time and given the chance to choose one, even though you are quite capable of choosing. Some treats are better than others, and how else can you indicate your preferences?

What you would really adore is to have your treat wrapped up in layers of parcels — in tea cloths in paper bags in cardboard boxes tied with string — which you can tear and shake about until you reach the treat. Or perhaps you would like your treat to be broken up into pieces and placed around the house, on nose-high furniture edges, so you have to go off and sniff for them. "Sniff-and-seek", let's call it. But you won't get anything like that if you're living under Stodgy.

Suggested strategy: Do something unexpected. When you're inside, yodel or wolf-howl at your treat or bone: they'll wonder why you're doing it, and wondering about you is a start. At least it will serve to remind them exactly what type of vertebrate you are. When you're outside, try scratching or leaping at the door and when the Stodge comes to open it, run away. Then when the Stodge comes out, let him or her chase after you. It may dawn on the Stodge that you've invited them to play, and they may realize that you have an imagination. After that, they may decide to develop one of their own.

The Absentee

This person never seems to have enough time for you. Or indeed, *any* time for you. They are always bursting through the door and squealing the tires, late for the appointments that they chronically overbook. This person's calendar looks like someone is using it to write a thriller, having run out of regular paper: it's full of codes, initials, and exclamation marks ("buy T. P. for the W. C., A. S. A. P!") No doubt very exciting for the Absentee, but when they are M. I. A. it's a sad situation for you. There you stand, hopeful despite constant disappointment, with your leash between your teeth and a brand new toy between your paws. You can't actually *play* with the toy because it's still stuck round with little spikes of white plastic, attaching price tag, material disclosure, and a warning about having too much fun.

<u>Suggested strategy</u>: There are two approaches you may wish to take. One is very energetic, and the other is more laid back.

Approach No. 1: Whenever this human dresses to go out, get up on your back legs and embrace them round the hips (or legs, if you're short). When they protest that they have to tie their shoes, pay no attention but hug their shoulders with your paws (they'll probably be sitting down, so this will be easy), and lick their faces repeatedly.

Remember to breathe, but keep the licking up, nonstop. It will delay their exit for a minute or two, since it's very hard to get ready when a dog is blocking the way and fogging their glasses. At a certain point you will have to stand down, and they will leave as planned, but your desperate actions may at last have a beneficial effect. The thought may eventually sink in that "perhaps I should spend more time with my dog. Play with him more, talk to him more. Anything to keep this slobber off my chin/tie/scarf/blue suede shoes."

Approach No. 2: Flatter your human as much as you can. Snuggle up with them when they're reading a magazine; sit sweetly by them when they're drinking coffee; gaze adoringly at them as they do the laundry. Human beings need to feel important, especially where dogs are concerned. If you can make them believe that they are the lodestar of your life, your chief joy and the reason you get up every morning, that will make them feel all's right with the world. And having a keener sense of the bond between you will make them think twice about deserting you. Never forget the guilt factor. It is *always* on your side.

The Sofa Growth

Also known as the Sofa Sloth or Couch Potato, this human is often very companionable. Because they are addicted to the sofa — indeed, their body shape somewhat resembles it — they can't be bothered to

rouse themselves enough to stop whatever mischief you get up to. On the other hand, they are inconsiderate: too lazy to find a treat for you while they're getting another bag of popcorn. The TV, which is always on, is loud and unsettling, and what's more, you see barely any dogs on it. It's true that you can find plenty to do while the Sofa Growth is in position, but now and then you would rather like some actual quality time with your human. A game of chase, for instance, or a decent walk in an interesting setting. Is it hopeless? Probably.

Suggested strategy: Obviously, since the TV is getting between you and your human, you need to get between your human and the TV. There are two useful ways of doing this, one being more drastic than the other.

The gentlest mode of interference is to stand in front of the screen whenever commercials come on. If you're a little dog, stand up on your hind legs. The sudden sight of you, real as life and more poignant than a soap opera, may shake the Sofa Growth out of their torpor. For the moment they may be grateful that you've provided something pleasant to look at, and that may even remind them of their true priorities.

You can tell the onset of commercials because the screen becomes flashier and louder, there is a sense of restlessness in the air, and your human is fumbling for the remote. If you honestly can't tell a commercial from the Sofa Growth's chosen fare, then stand in front of the television anyway. Given the frequency of commercials, chances are you'll have perfect timing.

Of course, there is a more direct line of treatment, and you don't need me to tell you what it is. That's right: Hide the remote. This is not as cruel as it sounds. In fact it could be said that, since the Sofa Growth's life functionally depends on it, you have an actual *obligation* to put the remote out of sight. Expect hours and days of grumpiness while they search in vain for it, and keep a low profile. But understand that you are helping them to break their addiction, and it'll the do the world of good for you as well.

The Camp Director

A driven athlete, busybody, or do-it-yourselfer, this human would not know what to do with five minutes of rest and is determined to make sure that you don't get any, either. Much of their free time is occupied in flinging their own body parts around, in whatever fad exercise is popular this year, but other activities include power-washing, tree lopping, and re-tiling the roof, supplemented by the sawing of bricks in case they should ever need a chicken house. Quieter times are not very quiet, either: they expel so much breath into their mobile phone, the police could use it in lieu of a breathalyzer in the event of a driving accident.

The Camp Director insists that you join him or her in everything they do. Believing that a moment spent away from them is a wasted moment of your life, they strap you into every vehicle they're operating — be it a tractor, mower, or high-speed motorboat — and expect you to enjoy the ride. If they  see your eyelids start to droop, they are seized with panic that they may be "boring" you, or even worse, "neglecting" you. Their behaviour at these times can be frankly irrational, such that they start banging pots and pans simply to keep you awake. They have no idea whatever that doggies like to flop. In a word, they're a nightmare. Can anything be done about them?

Suggested strategy: Chew their shoes. I don't mean just one pair, I mean the lot: trainers, hiking shoes, surf waders, steel-toed work boots. They can't do anything without them, and they may just get the sneaking suspicion that you're trying to tell them something – like "take a break". If they are more of an athlete than a DIYer, liking martial arts or power yoga where shoes aren't required, then you have but one alternative: chew the belt or the mat. If they're a cyclist, chew the tires. That'll show them! Oh, but I was wrong about chewing *all* their shoes. If they've got a pair of slippers, you ought to spare them.

The Feckless Leader

Dog experts (or rather, experts on dogs) are always telling humans that they must take charge, lead the pack, direct and guide their dog through life, and otherwise be the guarantor of their safety, health, and happiness. Would that it were always so. The Feckless Leader has very little passion for this role, and almost no interest in learning how to fulfill it. A dog to this person is an afterthought, an accessory to a lifestyle. "Here is my loft, my canopy bed, my decorative pillows, and my dog". The dog is merely a follow-on from other events: marriage, house, children, trampoline or playground set.

The practical consequences for you are that this human is inattentive. More often than not, the water in your bowl is stale, with bits of whatever garden flora you've been nibbling floating in it. By contrast, the attentive human knows that when it comes to water, you demand fresh, and given the choice you would rather have it mineraled, preferably from a mountain spring and preferably sparkling.

Squirrels: They look so innocent, but *you* know otherwise.

A baby is always a baby, though. This California one is just a baby, so you wouldn't chase it, would you?
Would you?

The fact that you snack on weeds and sniff dead squirrels has absolutely nothing to do with it. But to the Feckless Leader, you're "just a dog", so what does it matter anyway? This person can hardly be bothered to take you for a walk, preferring to let you run off-leash near traffic and cliff edges, simply because it's easier for them. Indeed, the Feckless Leader is usually clueless with a leash, choosing the wrong length and style, keeping it taut when it ought to be slack, and droopy when you need reeling in. We have all seen dogs being pulled around to such an extent that only two paws were on the ground, and sometimes none at all. The Feckless Leader doesn't even notice, since their mind is on a million other things. Do you have personal experience of this? Have a good cry and let it all out.

Suggested strategy: There are at least three ways to cope with a careless human. Firstly, hope and pray that over time yours will come to love you, really and truly and not just because you're cute. With real love comes a desire to learn more about you and a wish to serve you better. The Feckless Leader is a tough case but not a hopeless one. Secondly, Feckless Leaders usually don't live alone, but have several friends and family members that you might bump into on the porch or on the stairs. Some of these people will even be responsible, loving, and serious-minded. Identify these people, and firmly resolve to make yourself their very best friend. Over time, one of them may find that they can't live without you, and beg your Feckless Leader to let you come and live with them. Your third option is simply to wait your owner out: eventually they may tire of their burdens (meaning you), at which point you may get lucky and find yourself rehomed.

*China chopstick-rest on the left;
ornamental wire poodle, right.
One way or another, humans
must have dogs around them!*

The Fusspot

Even dogs can acknowledge that they are not the most sensitive interior decorators, but the Fusspot has a horror of every physical contribution the dog makes to life at home. Shredded shopping bags are an "unholy mess" and toys lying about are "a shambles", but what this person really abhors are the traces of your DNA. These are strewn around the house in the form of hair, drool, dander (only slightly better than dand*ruff*), and uneaten bits of rawhide. The Fusspot nearly had a nervous breakdown when you were a puppy in training and there were accidents on the carpet, but your metabolism still keeps them busy with sweeping, swabbing, disinfecting, and vacuuming. When you sneeze, which often happens on account of the deodorizing powder, they say "Gezundheit". When you have a drink, they are standing by with a towel, wiping your flews so that drips from them won't leave a trail on the floor.

This is understandable, and doesn't bother you at all; it's the weekly full-body bathing that you honestly find too much. The shampoo is slowly eroding you, and replacing all your natural layers with a strange concoction like embalming fluid. Besides the appalling smell (Lavender & Rose) and the equally appalling itch, you face a good deal of social embarrassment. It's not so much the lavender stink – if mingled with dust and acquired honourably, by trampling in the garden, lavender daubs the dog with a certain glamour. It's the rose stink that ruins your reputation, since without any corresponding scratches you just come across as prissy.

However, the worst part of living with Fusspot is not even the obsession with hygiene. The thing that really gets up your nose is that so much of the house is off-limits. You're not allowed on any sofa or chair. You get slippered if you're spotted in the bedroom. You are scolded for loitering in the kitchen. You're shooed from the table. And so on. Your only safe option is your basket, but even a basket-loving dog likes to stretch their legs now and then, and take a stroll down the corridor to see what the laundry room is doing (think of all those dirty socks!). But guess what? You're not allowed near the laundry, either. Even when it's clean.

Suggested strategy: To quell the excessive bathing, you should try to relocate it from the house to the patio or porch outside. When you go for walks, seek all the muddiest tracks, and if there is any water lying about, make sure you get splashed with it. When you return home, the Fusspot won't want your filthy paws on their immaculate parquet, to say nothing of their Persian carpet, and will resolve to wash you outdoors. This is to your advantage for three reasons: 1) it's much easier to run away, since you can't be dungeoned in a bath; 2) they will probably resort to treats to keep you hanging round; 3) as soon as you are clean, you can rush right off into the bushes and restore your respectable doggy smell. Chances are that the struggle will so exhaust the Fusspot, they'll find some hygienic reason to bathe you less often.

To loosen the room restrictions, play the demure lamb who would never dream of trespassing. When your Fusspot leaves the premises – they can't be there every minute of the day – sit languidly in your basket. The moment you can no longer hear the car engine, leap up and go on a snooping spree. (Leave the beds alone; it'll give the game away.) Keep an ear out for the engine, and when you hear it again, take the necessary action. By the time they have turned the key in the door, there you are like a perfect darling, sitting languidly again in your basket.

The Lordly Lord

This human feels attached to you and wants to include you in his (or her) life, yet often leaves you feeling neglected and disregarded. The Lordly Lord can be seen as a less extreme version of the Camp Director and the Feckless Leader, rolled into one. He views you in much the same way as Sherlock Holmes views Watson – the doctor that apparently has no life of his own, and exists only to do whatever Holmes wants him to do. So when Holmes declares that it's time to wade through London fog or stalk a dark mansion from a corpse-ridden graveyard, armed only with a ridiculous hat and a revolver (you squeeze one end and it goes bang at the other), the doctor had better be ready. Holmes is never interested in the fact that perhaps Watson had other plans for that evening, such as sitting in a comfy chair in his cosiest dressing gown, stuffing his beard with brandy chocolates and getting slightly squiffy. Even less would Holmes imagine a private rendezvous with someone wholesome, toothsome and awesome, who looked good in pearls and had no mustache.

The practical effect for you is that the Lordly Lord sees you as an adjunct to whatever he feels like doing, and it's your job to tag along, happily or not. It isn't bedtime until *he's* sleepy, and in the meantime, he never thinks to turn a lamp off or dim the lights or turn down the noise for your sake. Even though you might have had a long day of leaping encouragingly while he does jumping jacks, waiting by the door while he's out enjoying his freedom, and escorting him whenever he takes the trash out, he expects your body clock to mesh with *his*. (On the other hand, when he's hungover he expects you to lie about all day while he groans and drinks an orange-juice aspirin cocktail. He doesn't add "hair of the dog": you're it, letting him use you as a pillow.)

The one thing you can say about the Lordly Lord is that he doesn't let *your* needs get in the way of his own. In fact, he finds it hard to remember that you have desires or recall what they are. While he's sitting on a park bench, stuffing himself with a pork pie, Scotch egg, potato crisps and sausage roll, you're lucky if you can catch the crumbs. While he's swilling some ghastly brown concoction that is loaded with food colouring, afloat with carbon dioxide, and rich in aspartame, he doesn't care that you're panting for your life in the little patch of shade the tree provides. He wouldn't think or trouble himself to bring a bottle of water and a bowl for you, so *you* can have a drink on a warm day. (Much less would he slip in some ice.) He wouldn't cut short the picnic for your benefit, either. All you can do is wait until he's bored and wants to go home, at which point you can stagger up to your water bowl and hope it hasn't dried out in the last several hours.

Suggested strategy: Remind the Lord in an active way that you're a person, too. At night, when you're tired of the commotion and bright lights and desperately want some peace, find a high-visibility spot and pretend to fall asleep in it. This might be on the sofa next to your Lord, or on your personal lounger or even in his lap. Twitch your paws, race your legs a little and murmur, as if you're dreaming of chasing rabbits. If this fails to get his attention, woof a few times and then snore, loudly. If you interfere with the re-runs he's watching – *Great Moments In Football Fumbles* and the like – he may decide to let you escape to another room where it's actually darkish and quietish.

As for food and drinks, you should show your face whenever he's having any, and follow him frequently to the fridge door or the sink. Gaze up at him as he pours a glass of something, even if it's frothy and malty and he tells you it's not for doggies. Sit by him attentively whenever he fixes a snack. To help him get the message, stick your tongue out and lick your lips. It's a cliché of hunger that Ghengis Khan's dog used in 1192, but it works.

These may seem like small, inconsequential tactics. But very soon, each display of your personhood, like a single bird hardly noticed, will add up to many birds and have a have a cumulative effect.

Your Lord will become aware that it's not just *his* needs that matter. *Your* needs will be strewn across his vision like flocks filling the sky or gaggling at the water's edge. Like their bodies, your needs will be impossible to miss!

The Distracted Missionary

This is a wonderful human: free with her time, generous with her home, and willing to share her kitchen with dogs, cats, rabbits, budgies, marmosets, lorises, and fish tanks. Well, perhaps not the last three. Though it feels like it, when her relatives come to visit.

So what's the problem? Large-hearted person, sharing her all with all and sundry. Well, *that's* the problem. However loving this person is, and however charitable, you always have to share the love and the charity with the other assorted orphans that she has taken in. What is more, she is so busy and socially stretched that she gets a little mixed up. (What is the cat's dinner doing in *your* bowl?) The Distracted Missionary, caught between earning a living and rescuing the needy, gets forgetful and scatty. For the most part, you enjoy belonging to a big, bouncy tribe of animals (even if Phineas the guinea-pig does nothing but twitch his nose.)

Yes, these kid goats are gorgeous. Charming, and with glossy coats to die for.
But they're still *goats*. And you're a dog. You could never be Top Goat – or could you…?

But the little secret you hardly dare admit is that only *half* of you wants to be a raisin in the big cake that is The Addams or The Munsters family. The other half wants to be The Princess With Her Slipper, the beautiful soul that is more wonderful than the others, fated for happiness ever after in a palace of magic smells, soft beds, and frequent pizza delivery.

You don't feel special when you're Reject Intake No. 8 or Rescue No. 9 in the home of the Distracted Missionary. *Other* dogs get whatever's going: the hugs and kisses, the place of honour on the boat's bow, the best seat in the car, the choice lounging place on the deck, or the armchair of the summer hotel with scenic overlook. You all have to take it in turns or jostle for position. Your human simply doesn't have *time* to give you much individual consideration and attention. Or, for that matter, much you-directed *affection*. She's petting you and saying "good boy, Billy", but it might just as well be "good boy, Willy" (the ferret) or "good girl, Filly" (the seahorse in the tank). It's even worse when your human forgets who she's talking to and calls out "Come on, Bobby"; I'll spare you embarrassment by not stating what species Bobby is.

<u>Suggested strategy</u>: Be a love-bomb. The way to distinguish yourself from all the other occupants of the household is by being more loving, more cheerful, and more *present* than anybody else. When your human gets home, be the first at the door, greeting her rapturously with spins, twists, shimmywags and kisses. Be prepared to do a little waltz, your front paws in her hands. Humans adore this. Otherwise, employ the other suggestions in this guide for  getting on with people, and perform them very consciously, not skipping a day, even if you feel lazy. Always beg with your eyes, not with your voice; but do use your voice in other ways. If you are pleased with something and you want to show your human that you appreciate the cushion, the treat, or the chest rub, then I advise a "snurgle". It's a cross between a purr and a gurgle, and reassures your human that she is doing the right thing, which is enormously gratifying for her. The conviction she develops that she is your favourite creature in the entire world will soon make you *her* favourite creature in the entire world. It may even lead to the thought that when Randy, Frosty, and Stanford finally pass on, there's no need for her to replace them, because she's got *you*. Chances are, however, that there will always be lovies and dovies in the Distracted Missionary's life, but at least you'll always be Top Dog.

The Show-Off

Also known as the Drill Sergeant, this person is widely reputed, over about three neighbourhood blocks, to have highly disciplined dogs that know the Voice of Command when they hear it. Well, *most* dogs know a Voice of Command, but *these* dogs actually obey. (For the Show-Off, two or three are better than one.)

The Show-Off makes sure that you know several tricks, which you are made to perform whenever a visitor comes round. If a group of dogs and humans are gathered sociably on someone's lawn, the Show-Off will be sure to spot them through his binoculars and turn up promptly with his act – namely, you. But the Show-Off won't greet the others until he has their attention first. Ostentatiously, the Show-Off strolls across the road alone, leaving you off-leash on the other side, having drummed it into you long ago that you may only cross the road when told. The neighbours take notice and watch, expectant and hushed. The seconds pass, ponderous as mammoths tramping through snow to their wintering grounds. And then, like the matron elephant trumpeting with her trunk, the Show-Off gives the signal. You cross. Ta-dah *dum*. Although the other humans have a good word and a pat for you, it's understood who the real star is.

Day-to-day life with a Show-Off need not be tiresome, but his ego is the crocodile in the bathroom that is sometimes hard to get around. He delights in giving commands just because he can, especially if others are watching. So you do the "down" for no particular reason, other than to satisfy your human's sense that he really is the Top Dog. Does he ever catch the roll of your eyes that says, "Oh, come off it, boss"?

English gargoyle does a sort of "down", without looking the least bit submissive.

<u>Suggested strategy</u>: A good way to deal with this type is to show him up now and then, precisely at the moments when he wants to show off. Obey him during drills and (mainly) around the house, but studiously ignore him when he issues orders in front of others, solely for the purpose of showing off. When you hear "sit", remain standing and investigate someone's trouser-leg instead. When you hear "give me your paw", raise your left one uncertainly, drop it quickly as a hand reaches out to grasp it, and then raise your right paw. Repeat, switching paws. Keep this up until the humans involved decide that it's pointless to carry on. Finally, if the Show-Off has the temerity to require of you a "down", give him a withering look and find a place to piddle instead. By the time that's over, the conversation with his chosen audience will have moved on to other things.

Remember, the time to disobey or bungle his commands is when someone outside the household is on the scene. This is important for two reasons: 1) public flubs will discourage him, since no one enjoys looking foolish, and 2) he won't dare discipline you, since other people despise a cruel taskmaster and he can't risk giving the impression of being one. He also knows, as a matter of fact, that disciplining you later won't do any good: correction must follow error without delay. Besides, he doesn't *want* to be cruel. He only wants to be full of himself, and for that he needs your help. Don't give it.

Photo: The Dog Collar Museum, Leeds Castle Foundation, Kent, England

These are from centuries past, when "guarding" meant more than barking at the postman. The top collar's central ring looks suspiciously useful for a chain, and there's no give in the fastening. The other cuff collars have a similar "you will tell us where the secret plans are" feel. But look at the link collar: this is dressing you up as a barbed wire fence with drool. Imagine jangling like a jailor all day!

Accepting Your Human's Limitations

We have canvassed several types of humans, though there are many more in existence, some of whom are angels, and some of whom ought to have their picture on the local S. P. C. A. dartboard. The humans described above are neither angels nor monsters, but somewhere in between, and they do all have their good points.

All dogs must be forgiving, in a general way, but you should also try to accept your human's particular limitations. I'm afraid that even if the Stodge eventually discovers the meaning of play, they will never think to have a pillow-fight with you (and wouldn't agree to it if they did). And dressing up as a wild boar so you can pretend to attack them is utterly out of the question. (Snorting boarishly may, however, happen one fine day.) The Fusspot will never be relaxed about black paw-prints on the bedding, nor will they gaze indulgently on the dictionary you've rearranged, page by page, and left in a heap on the floor. Don't get down about this. Look on the bright side and remember their kindnesses, like the time you ate their antique butterfly collection, and they still fed you that evening, anyway.

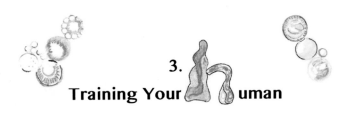

3.
Training Your Human

The Art Of Begging

This is the fundamental art, but many dogs aren't very good at it. Studies have shown that pushy dogs often fail in their quest; but, more surprisingly, so do those dogs that merely gaze hopefully at the desired food, neglecting to lock eyes with their people and sustain the right sort of tension. Does this sound familiar? Are your begging attempts too hit-and-miss? Let's investigate what you are doing wrong, and suggest what you need to do in order to bring home the bacon.

First, realize that begging is not a talent contest. You don't get extra points – or bacon – for a rich, dynamic performance. Pacing may make you more visible, but it doesn't make you more irresistible. And any kind of vocalizing – especially whining – imperils the success of your mission. It cannot be emphasized too strongly that the first secret of a profitable beg is *absolute silence*. However tempted you are to whinge, whine, whimper, or bleat, clamp down on your vocal folds instanter. Your motto should be: "my lips are sealed, unless they're receiving something".

The second secret is rather more subtle. *Employ emotion*, which is to say, *act*. Act like a poor waif orphan, left on the doorstep in a blanket, who has never had a decent meal in its whole life and probably never will. The fact that you are a loved and pampered dog is neither here nor there. Your humans, of all people, know just how much you are *not* a poor Oliver Twist, and yet, astoundingly, they will somehow momentarily believe it. They will give in. The icy wall between licit and illicit will simply melt to the floor, and it's your big, waifish eyes that will do the melting. A 1-2-3 tail wag, backing up your gaze, is also a gosh-darn cute way of saying "one for me?".

Some dogs vary their begging routine. Instead of impersonating the poor waif orphan, they employ a more detached pose that says, "Just looking". They're still talking with their eyes, of course, but it's a different story they're telling. "Don't mind me. I'm not asking for any food, which looks fabulous, by the way. I don't need a smidge of a succulent morsel, I just want to look at it. Wow, is that steak? Beautiful chargrill stripes. Gosh, you really know how to cook. But pretend I'm not here...".

The thing to understand is that humans *want* to give you their people-food, they just feel guilty about doing it. Your job is to make it easier for them to give in to their natural inclinations. When you are politely imploring, or pretending not to implore at all, you are rewarded with that delicious mashed potato. *They* are rewarded by seeing *you* rewarded. Everybody benefits.

A final piece of advice: Don't beg at the dining table. Or even the breakfast table. In fact, try to avoid tables altogether. The same piece of chicken that might be given grudgingly (or not at all) at the table, once the humans have sat down to eat, would slip from their hands much more freely right by the oven. If this sounds inconsistent — well, that's humans for you.

Are You Getting Out Enough?

Picture the scene: somewhere within a thick canopy of trees, surrounded by mountains and a fish-filled river, there is a chalet with decking all around it. The sun is shining, the bees are buzzing, and everything should be wonderful – except that you are stuck behind a window, and no one will agree to let you out. It's true that there is a large bear on the other side, which you of course were the first one to know about. But there was barely time to bark, "declare yourself, stranger!" when the humans came and hauled you away. From behind the glass, you've been adamant that the stranger must push off, but he hasn't, choosing to linger by the grill and slurp up the cooking oil instead. The house is in an uproar, and no one will venture out. You, if let loose, would be able to set things right, but you need to get eyeball to eyeball. No chance of that. Sigh. You know that the stranger must be laughing, and since his next stop is the river, he'll be laughing all the way to the bank.

Fortunately, events like this are as rare in your household as toothpaste with roast peanut flavour. (You quite like peanuts, but your human always buys the one that tastes vaguely of geriatric poultry.) Bear in mind, *every* dog faces constriction at times. The question is whether, on normal, no-bear days, you feel that you're getting out enough. And if you aren't, what can you do about it?

Those dogs that live on ranches or large estates, or near great woods, don't have to fret about getting their fun and freedom. A door is opened – be it cottage or castle – and out they go. How much effort does it take a human simply to open a door? The trouble comes for most dogs when humans have to leash them and personally take them on a walk. You would think that this would be

easy: humans, being bipeds, are biologically advanced at putting one foot in front of the other. Yet people, though committed to their jobs and ready enough to toil for their families, are often lazy when it comes to you, the dog. It's that consistency issue again. Are you less beautiful than the family baby? No. Are you less fun than the annual dog show? No. So what is the fuss all about?

A recent survey of dog owners (all ages and sexes, urban and rural) revealed several reasons for reluctance to walk the dog. In order, here are the top five.

Reason No. 1. Bad weather, e.g. hail, sleet, driving rain, lightning, or a faint grey wash on the horizon. Some in hot climates could not bear going out when the mercury hit 80, or, on the low end, 60.

Reason No. 2. Dog sniffs every bird-dropping, lamppost, and clump of shrubbery. Sits to watch the neighbourhood patrol car crawl along the road. Stops to assess flattened frog's state of dessication; observes a lawn-mower going back and forth. Watches stray feathers blowing. Hardly any progress can be made. Owner gets no exercise on these "walks".

<u>Reason No. 3</u>. Owner dislikes exercise. Also, dog is too lively or perky, moves too fast, and wants to make too much progress. (Note: Many of those surveyed should have claimed No. 3 instead of No. 2, but preferred to fib.)

<u>Reason No. 4</u>. Dog's walking manners are appalling. Strains on lead; runs after bicycles; leaps on people at the slightest sign of friendliness; is always well behind or well ahead of the owner. Dog returns from this ordeal feeling, on the whole, rather refreshed; owner returns needing a long hot shower and an alcoholic beverage.

<u>Reason No. 5</u>. Owner wishes to avoid neighbours, on account of disputes/incompatible dogs/invitations to block parties. Can't spare the extra 40 minutes needed for a round trip to the nearest park. Dog ends up spending much of their time by the driveway gate, looking out longingly and barking. Human has attacks of guilt and takes dog on walks occasionally.

❧ One hot human and his hot dog

Friends, I cannot deceive you. If you are not getting out enough, there is very little you can do, besides being lovable and well behaved, to spur your human into action.

The *quality* of your walk-life, however, is in your power to change. How do you improve it? We'll discuss techniques in the next chapter. They work, and don't ever feel that you shouldn't resort to them. "Walking the dog" is done for *your* benefit, and if you wish to look at lizards, visit tree trunks, examine snails and scout for robins, why shouldn't you?

We have all heard about missing bodies being found by "a man out walking his dog" – not the *same* man, but it's usually men that wander off the beaten path: women have more sense. Anyway, *you* know and I know that it's the dog that really found the body. The man just happened to be there at the other end of the lead. And yet, do the papers ever say "Alpie, a Bernese mountain dog aged 3, cracks difficult case"? Do we ever read "Fenton, a black Lab with a taste for adventure, pursued trail of justice"? And what about the Stone Age cave paintings of Altamira in Spain? Dogs found those, and humans followed. Keep sniffing and be proud, I say.

Walkies Management

As a technical, juridical matter, humans are in charge of any walk with you. *They* may be strapped into watches, thongs, bras, and Y-fronts, and trussed about with necklaces, waist pouches, shoulder bags, and trouser belts – to say nothing of being weighted by portable phones, wallets, plastic, coinage and keys – but the collar's on *your* neck, not theirs.

Appearances, of course, are deceiving. A fruit fly may appear to be bathing luxuriously in wine, but in fact he's merely waiting to be rescued by a fingertip – and then, shaking off the damp and humiliation, to stagger away drunkenly till he makes the same mistake tomorrow night. (Fruit flies have very poor manners and even worse memories.) Happily *you*, besides being too big to fall into a goblet, have a lot more salsa in the brain department. But it's no good having a cunning mind if you don't know how to use it. By mastering a few simple techniques, you can get your own way much more often.

Let's start with a common scenario. Your human doesn't want to walk down a particular lane because it's crowded, smelly, and there's a dog that barks on the corner. You *do* want to walk down the lane because it's crowded, smelly, and you *like* the dog on the corner. If you don't act assertively, chances are that you will never sniff that trash can or wag at that dog again. Something must be done. Fortunately, there are several ploys available to you.

1. Feign temporary deafness. When your human called "come on, Gadzooks", you didn't hear because of the passing truck/dog barking on the corner/Canada geese squawking overhead. In the meantime, you have covered several more feet and the momentum is now in your chosen direction.

2. Pretend to be particularly interested in wildlife or the cat across the road, even if you and the cat have exchanged glowers of contempt that day already. They are all merely decoys, providing an excuse to make a dash for it in the direction of your choice. Again, by the time you have hounded four squirrels up trees, disturbed a flock of birds, and the cat has slinked off to sun itself, you are that much further down the street.

Cat: the only creature in the world that can still be superior while lying on its back.

3. Refuse to be yanked by your collar and, if necessary, sit or lie down. Humans hate this. When you are on a long lead, it's a bother for them to come back to you, and it's even more of a bother to get you up. At this point you should act as if you've never heard the "stand" command before, and chances are, it's been such a long time since your human last used it – if they ever used it at all – that they can't fault you for not comprehending. Naturally, bigger dogs will find the lie-down tactic more useful than small dogs will, their extra pounds being so much more difficult to shift. Small dogs would do well to get up very quickly, run a short distance, and then lie down again.

Of course, the run-and-flop method isn't right for every outing. When you are in the mood for a contemplative stroll, just slow down. Like a grouper fish in a French immersion class, you will not care about the speed of those chattering around you; and just as the grouper's mouth keeps slowly shutting and dropping open, you will refuse to jog along or otherwise keep up with your human.

Slow down, turn your nose up, sniff the air disdainfully, let your paws sink into the ground as if it's quicksand slathered in glue, and stand there stubbornly. Now don't tell me you can't do that, because I *know* you can! Take a hint from dog-yoga and just let your body go: like a tank on thin ice, or a puppet when its hand has gone to sleep. Even if you're still in an upright position, there just won't be any budging you.

Your human will realize soon enough that you have not merely paused to sniff a passing car tire or examine an interesting bird splat. To the contrary: your straight-ahead gaze, combined with your stolid pose, declares your opposition to any forward movement. And unless your human decides that they will brook no opposition, you may find that they fall in with your desire.

On occasion you may need to up the ante, however. When Mrs Shinyboots insists on leading you down a garden path that is utterly devoid of dog scents and other wonders of nature, then a stronger approach is called for. If your human is unacquainted with dog-yoga and fails to respond to the signs, yanking you by the collar, the next step is to lower your head like a bull about to charge. This action declares: "You can try to pull me, but I'm braced and ready to resist all coercion. I want to go my own way. So yank my collar, if you dare. Go ahead, make my neck ache!" Your human will find it hard to take up this challenge, even though they know you've got a neck like the Eiffel Tower. The charging-bull pose is usually enough to make them concede, but if it isn't, I suggest tossing your head from side to side, as if you have a horse-mane for a wig and you're acting in an epic film.

By this stage, your human should be happy to give in. They will come up with all sorts of acceptable justifications for so doing. Your superior nose, they will pretend, has caught the scent of danger beyond. Or perhaps you are suffering: hot, cold, tired, thirsty, or fed up with their diatribe, as they rant about their utility bill and then pretend to be giving you orders whenever a stranger comes by. Perhaps they will simply tell themselves (and you, to deflate your victory) that they have an important rolling pin or manicure kit to nab on eBay, anyway.

These boots weren't made for walking – they were made for shopping. But don't let them win The Battle Of The Walk!

The methods I've suggested here won't always work; you must judge whether conditions are ripe and act accordingly. But it doesn't matter much if you fail. Most humans would prefer to please their dogs, and if they must deny you in one way, odds are that they'll make it up to you in another.

Sign washed up on English coast

Limiting the Number of Commands

I bet you've noticed that humans are extremely fond of commands. Couldn't get through the day without them, in fact. And instead of simply adopting the old standbys – "give", "stay", and "leave it", for example – they seem to enjoy inventing new ones, whether achievable or not. So you may hear things like "fetch slippers, the red ones", or "wag at Uncle John", or "wipe your feet". If your human is determined to impose on you some new command, then you may at last have to learn it. But that's a shark fin on a far horizon, a tiger tongue behind glass at the zoo. Nothing really to worry about. I am going to share two highly effective ways of limiting the commands you are subject to. Both of them require that you not reveal just how well you understand the situation.

First and most obviously, let your mind wander during training sessions. When the human gets your attention again, give them a look that says, "I'm sorry – I missed that". When they drill you (for the sixteenth time) with "shut the door", give them another look that declares, "I'm just a canine and I'm all confused, like a duck that's been holding its breath under water too long. How am I ever going to get this?". Your human, who had previously rated you the René Descartes of dogdom, now thinks that even *rubber* ducks might possibly be swifter than you.

In truth, by now you have grasped the concept of "shut", and you know perfectly well what a door is, having found the door in the fence at the park that leads to a secret garden full of rabbits, sprinklers, and doves. When your human mentioned "door" at the time, you knew exactly what they were talking about. But that was then, when it was convenient to be in the know; and this is now, when it isn't.

In any case, the woozy duck impression will serve you well, sandbagging your human's expectations and certainly her enthusiasm. She will probably abandon "shut the door", since it would be easier just to do it herself!

The second way to limit the number of commands is

to have ears only for the right ones. Distracted by daily life, humans bungle their own commands – momentarily forgetting the code words that they themselves have set up, in order to have you do or cease doing a certain activity.

Thus, when they want you to fetch a pathetic twig they've tossed, they shout "Go get it!" instead of "Fetch!" When they see you playing with a full plastic bottle, which is punctured and leaking all over the floor, they shout

"*Oh, no!*" instead of "Leave it!"

"*Would you knock it off!*" replaces "Quiet!" and so on.

Now, you are under no obligation to respond to these impromptu, confused barkings, even if you actually understand them. Unless you feel that kindness warrants it, never let on that you get the idea, but carry on unless and until you hear the established code words. Humans can be slack and sloppy, and must be taught proper form and discipline. Further, when humans are allowed to say anything they want, your command list will be long. When they must toe the line, your command list stays short. Which would you prefer?

Some people want to be a rolling stone. You'd rather be a rolling beach ball, like this one, set free by a tropical storm.

4.

How To Feel Happier At Home

Getting the Most
Out of Soft Furnishings

When I advise you to get the most out of soft furnishings – which is to say, anything you can sit on – I don't mean that you ought to tear at the covers and pull out all the stuffing. We are not talking about turning fat, overfull chairs and cushions into thin, emaciated ones. What we are talking about is your ease and comfort.

This is not to deny that some trampling may be required. For instance, in Figure 1 you see the feather sofa as the humans of the household intended it to be. Note the plump, upright pillows that rest against the back of the sofa.

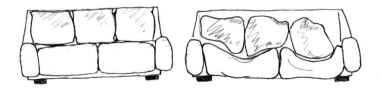

Fig. 1   Fig. 2

Passing to Figure 2, note the profoundly altered pillow shape and the squashed outline of the bottom or seat cushions. This result is known as <u>remodelling</u>, and the method used to achieve it, in this particular case, is known as <u>trampolining</u>.

What is the benefit to the dog? Well, when everything was in its human-appointed place, the back cushions were too high and pointy-edged to lie on, and there were no satisfactory headrests for a comfortably recumbent dog. The sofa surfaces were too flat and four-square, if you like. The remodelled sofa, however, provides opportunities for a number of different resting positions, with feet high and head down below, or vice versa. Can you imagine the dogs in Figure 3 being anything like as comfortable on the sofa as we see it in Figure 1?

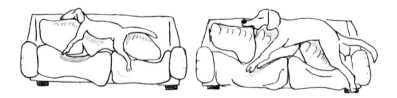

Fig. 3 (a): Medium to large dog   Fig. 3 (b): Giant dog

Fig. 3 (c): Little dog

What if you and your humans *don't* have feather-filled or mouldable kinds of furniture? What then? Well, a lot of dogs, whose homes feature leather or the stiffest of polyfoam couches – more like spinal-correction racks than anything else – just lie on the carpet. Or they make do with their beanbags or purpose-made dog loungers. Now, these can be very relaxing in their own way. But the fact is, *they're not the same.* These things are all right if you have a shoe you're working on (though you ought to resist shoes – see chapter five), and they're fine if you have a rawhide that's engaging your interest. Often they are good enough for a cat-nap, if you'll excuse the expression. But for really lush and fragrant comfort, there is nothing to equal a proper bed, by which I mean the sort that humans lie on.

It's an open secret that most dogs find their way onto the humans' bed, even if they are absolutely forbidden to do so. The real question is whether this is a frequent occurrence, or more difficult and rare than the journey of elephants to mine the salt caves of Mount Elgon. Let's say that your humans are resistant to letting you on the bed: What can you do?

My advice is never to attempt ensnugglement in a bed when your humans are not present. At least one human should be either in it or hovering in the vicinity. Furthermore, you want them to be relaxed, sleepy, possibly even tipsy, and inclined towards comfort rather than cleanliness. Most likely, this means that you will attempt to overcome their resistance at the *end* of the day, not at the beginning. In the morning, when they are in a more businesslike mood, their thoughts may incline toward order rather than comfort, and the virtues of pristine sheets will be much clearer. On the other hand, many dogs get their first haul-up on the mattress in the morning, when the sun is streaming through enchantingly, and the humans take pity on the poor dog who has had to sleep elsewhere all night. But again, whether your best opportunity is morning or night, you must wait till your humans are present. Why? Because they need to give their permission. If you just leap up of your own accord, or they find that you have done so in their absence, it is all too easy for them to feel that you have trespassed, or committed an act of *lèse majesté*, and they will simply take steps to prevent you from doing it again.

When they are admiring your charms, however, and feeling indulgent, *that's* when you should advance toward the bed and put your front paws up on the edge. Make eye contact – remember the bright, darling, hopeful eyes you deploy for begging – and wait there. Don't move. Let the air be breathless with expectation. The chances are very

good at this point that some loving arms will sweep down beside you, grasp your hind legs, and lift you resolutely onto the clouds of glory, otherwise known as the pillows and duvet. If it doesn't work the first time, repeat this procedure on another day. It takes great strength of will to refuse you, especially when you've asked so nicely.

Having More Toys and Games

In the course of doing research for this book, I met a delightful puppy named Betsy, who lives in California. (Names have been changed to protect her privacy and spare her people any mortification.) Betsy has a very nice life, but her feeding times are somewhat irregular. She has to remind her humans that it's time for dinner, as they are always busy and seem to forget. But often they don't take the hint. Jill just says "oh, hello, Betsy", and goes back to washing windows or whatever. Jack says "sorry, Betsy, I don't have time for walkies" – as if that's what she was after. And if she goes to the feeding table to rattle her empty bowl, her grandma says "Betsy, find a bone and settle down". So she does, because there's nothing else to do, except wait for the moment when someone asks "has anyone fed Betsy?".

portrait of Betsy by the author

Now, I mention Betsy's story because it's revealing, and not just about the issue of getting one's food in a timely manner. It reveals that games and toys are not quite prominent enough in her life. If Jill is up a ladder and Jack is in thrall to a brightly lit screen (as he generally is), then who is playing with Betsy? It's down to Grandma and the rawhide "bone", and though Grandma is a sweetheart and the bones she throws are welcome, there's still not much going on in the Fun & Games department.

It wasn't that Betsy's people hadn't bought her any toys – in fact, they had. But she showed me her toy box, and neither of us could work up much enthusiasm for its contents. There was a ghastly foul-smelling rubber thing, in no way enhanced by its squeaker. There was a pinwheel in garish colors of orange, pink, blue, banana-yellow and lizard-green, which was dazzling enough for the humans but less so for Betsy, whose eyes don't see the same hues (as you know). There was a dumpy giraffe that did nothing, though I could see that its neck had once been good for chewing. At the bottom was a sheep like a marshmallow, which didn't squeak, wasn't curly, and lacked legs, ears, or tail to take hold of. The sheep was such an absurdity that Betsy and I had to laugh. (Well, I laughed; Betsy just drifted off.) It's true that when we later found a long string to tie around it, the sheep became instantly better; but this is not much of a compliment to the sheep. In fact (yodel the following with any notes in any key):

Sing and blow trumpets
in praise of strings:
They make toys dangle,
they're marvellous things;
"Treasure whatever
the moment flings"–
Everything's better
on a string.

What difference does a string make? Well, it helps to turn a mere toy into a game — in this case, the game of "chase me while I dangle a sheep". Similarly, any toy can be jazzed up and made newly interesting by being pushed down a pantyhose leg and swung about the room. But since I was merely visiting and one doesn't need pantyhose in southern California, I'm afraid that Betsy still doesn't know this.

Fortunately for Betsy – and for you – the line between a toy and a game is very thin. There is no great distinction between them. Humans are quite different in this. They have creations they  call "antique bears", and dolls made of porcelain and fabric. These are toys, strictly speaking, but no one is allowed to play with them. Even when someone *did* play with them (back in the mists of history), swinging by the arms was frowned upon, and biting on the head was a definite, hysterical no-no. But if you can only play with toys by talking sweetly to them, what sort of game is that? In addition, humans speak of "collections", as in "my Barbie and Ken collection" or "my collection of glass frogs". As a dog, you are liberated from the need to collect. In fact, you crave newness and variety. Not for you the dumpy giraffe with the stunted legs and last month's slobber on it. You've got fresher, less conventional coconuts to crack.

This is why, when something is delivered to the house, the humans think that the package is for them, when really it's gift-time for you. There is a box – that's a toy – and paper wadding (toy) or perhaps some plastic air-strips or bubble-wrap (both toys). Savage the box – that's a game; and trail around the plastic, popping pieces as you go – that's a game also. It's free, and the humans planned to bin it, anyway. So you don't suffer any admonitions. What's more, it has all the things you like: funny textures, funny sounds, and thorough deconstruction.

It's not the content, it's the wrapping that counts!

Of course, the playful dog can't just rely on the availability of packages. So you have to look around (are you listening, Betsy?) to see what else might be made into a toy. If you like tugging and pulling, towels are a very good option – tea towels are not bad, and bath towels are even better. But the best thing is to get yourself a bra.

Cela n'est pas une brassière.

To the untutored eye this may look like a bra drying in the sun, but in fact it's a dog-toy in waiting.

Most bras have better stretch and recoil capacities than towels, and the cups are very useful for grasping, especially if lacy or padded. By this point you may be staring incredulously, asking how on earth you are really going to get hold of a bra – without bringing thunder down on you.

Well, it's not so daunting as it looks. As with getting access to beds, you will win the bra with human connivance and, ultimately, approval. You will do this by applying the toy-making principle: *prepare the item to become a toy before it officially IS one.* Thus, when your human is dangling the bra, with the intention of putting it on, you bite at it once or twice in a cheeky manner. Remember: no running off with it; it isn't a toy just yet. Your human will likely continue to put it on, but she'll have the thought in her mind: "I can tell that Betsy would love to play with this. Too bad it's mine, and she can't". And yet, unless the bra is a model they don't make now and it's perfect and she paid too much for it, the truth is that she soon will let you play with it, and it will be yours, and she'll no longer wear it. She won't be *able* to wear it, since the clasp will have been cut off for your safety.

This bra, it must be admitted, is not a likely candidate for toydom. It's not even practical as a *bra*, for heaven's sake. Be cheeky, but realize there are limits!

The same principle applies to pyjamas ("oops, my tooth got caught"), ties ("I just wondered what it tastes like"), and anything else you set your heart on. The item, after wear here and tear there, begins to have your name on it, so to speak. In the end, having your humans donate their own gear as toys saves them time and even money – money they would have spent on icky little monkeys or leaden balls that never leave the toy box.

Being a Fun-Magnet

There is one further idea that I'd like to suggest to Betsy and all those like her. We have to imagine now that you have been active in toy-and-game creation, but your humans have wandered and fun has dropped out of the agenda. They are all too busy "dual-tasking". Jill has put on her gardening gloves and her olive-oil-honey superhydrating hair mask. Jack is thinking or fantasizing in the office chair. Grandma is adjusting her designer bag and modelling it by the mirror in the hall. What now?

Clearly, you need to attract their attention again. If you merely saunter up to them, they'll just think that you feel like a saunter, assuming they notice you at all. If you whimper, they'll think you want a bladder break and offer to open the door. If you complain more urgently, they'll think that something's wrong and frown at you with concern. This won't do. You want a tactic that will catch their eyes within the limits of good taste, and you want to be compellingly adorable at precisely the same moment. You want them to stop whatever they're doing and come right over to you.

Sounds like a tall order? It isn't. Here's what to do: Flop on your back and wiggle. Wiggle your paws as well, if you're in the mood. Yes, you may feel silly at first, but not when you see the results. Humans can't resist a dog that's wiggling on the floor or the lawn, especially if said dog is their own. They go all squishy, and want to rub your tummy and kiss your face; they fall in love with your fabulous self all over again. In short, they become a sort of pliable dough, which is exactly how you want them.

Now, you may protest that this is all very well if *they* want a smooch with the pooch (or, if they're British, a snog with the dog), but it's useless if *you* want a frolic, complete with fake growls, leaps, and tumbles. The objection makes sense, but it's wrong. You need first of all to get your people's attention. When you are wiggle-scrumptious, your people are drawn to you like kittens to catnip, and that is half the task accomplished. But — and this is the crafty part — there's a piece of string hanging from your lips or a nice toy lurking nearby. Once the humans are down at your level, you can turn the lovey-doveyness to playfulness. When you leap up with the toy in your mouth and a frisky gleam in your eye, they will fall into play as readily as a bad skier falls into snow.

In sales rooms, this strategy is known as "bait and switch", but I don't think we need to accept this. It's not a sales pitch, it's an invitation — a "wiggletation", if you like.

A wiggletation in progress. Don't be fooled by the innocent expression and the whiteness of the paws: this dog is an expert.

Your Ally
In the Kitchen

Earlier we discussed the art of begging, and assumed a good rate of success if the right methods were applied. Yet even masters of the beg have been known to fail at times, and undoubtedly, you will, too.

A family party, for instance, which ought to be a flavour bonanza, can stymie your begging with its politics. Uncle John disapproves of steak at $30 a pound, and on top of that he disapproves of dogs. You won't be getting anything from *him*. Cousin Hayley loves you and usually gives you morsels, but not while Uncle John is playing defence. Uncle Will insists on bringing his cat whenever he comes to visit, and neither he nor Munchall have ever heard of sharing. And on it goes. So how, in this impossible scenario, are you to get a piece of the action?

The answer is simple: Hang around the dishwasher. You know, that trap-door in the kitchen, hiding the box where the scraps are kept. I know that the trap-door is mostly shut, but now and then it's bound to swing open. You just wait until someone – *not* Uncle John – decides to clean up the dishes. The trap-door has to stay open in order for the dishes to be stacked, and that's when you seize your chance. There will be plenty of crumbs, sauce, and gooey bits still clinging to the bowls and plates.

Remember when I said that dogs these days live in more luxury than ever? This is a case in point. Thirty years ago, a lot of people only washed their dishes by hand, so there was no chance of stealing a lick. And the old machines required that the plates be rinsed off first, which meant that every year, a ton of flavour literally was washed down the drain. Imagine this waste on a national, indeed an international, scale. But in the 21st century, dishwashers are so powerful that there is no need for a thorough scraping-off. The benefit to you? A veritable pantry of forbidden food, especially when your ally is around!

5.

Further Tips For Getting On With Humans

Choose Your Targets

When you have a nice set of fangs, as you, dear reader, probably do, it is one of life's pleasures to use them. But, as a considerate dog who really does love your humans, you nonetheless would do well to be judicious in your choice of targets. At the very least, rotate them: if you have put dents in the plantation shutters this week, then give it a rest next week, and chew on the chair legs instead. Neither behaviour will win you any accolades, but if you chew a little of this and a little of that, the chances are that some of the dents will go unnoticed. And when they *are* noticed, long afterwards, there may be doubt as to whether the culprit was you, or a visiting dog, or the dog that lived there before they moved in. On the other hand, if you keep going and going at the same object, you may be in danger of biting clean through or causing unsightly damage. The toothy puncture of a yielding object, such as a piano seat, is not likely to be overlooked – nor, in the case of valued upholstery, easily forgotten. Spare your humans (and yourself) the grief, and be a nibbler, not a canine Jaws.

It is disappointing, I know, but it must be said: shoes to human beings are sacrosanct. It's not that they *necessarily* value shoes above other things, since they would not be pleased to have chewed-up hats or masticated mittens. But unlike these other things, shoes tend to be low down or stored on the floor, which makes them especially vulnerable. If you have a hankering for some nice tasty leather, swallow that thought and find a foot to lick instead. You can't dig your teeth in, but the flavour is just as good or even better.

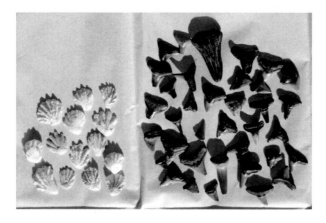

On the left: cat's paw shells. On the right: fossilized sharks' teeth, all from western beaches of Florida on the Gulf of Mexico. In your investigation of the household furnishings, aim to be delicate and choosy like the cat's paws, not ravening like the sharks' teeth.

Finally, a word about garden plants. Again, you should carefully choose your targets. Biting the heads off marigolds is no big deal, and eating hibiscus flowers may even be thought of as "cute". The digging-up of pinks and pansies *may* be considered venial, if they're already withered or "gone over"; and flattened impatiens, though they look a hopeless mess, can recover and bloom nicely again.

Left:
homegrown
oranges.

Right:
an "heirloom"
tomato. Hint:
heirloom means
"destroy at your peril!"

Otherwise, don't shred the ginger leaves, and refuse to damage orchard fruits, veggie plants, citrus, and peonies in flower. The latter take a long time to grow, from tender, uncertain buds, and if you come pillaging at the last moment, your human will see you as Godzilla. Of course, you are and always will be more important than any plant. Just don't make your human think about it.

Eschew the Grass- and Mud- Munching Habit

We all know that dogs make better worm-watchers than plane-spotters. Let flight machines roar overheard as they may, the moving and shaking and goings-on of life are generally, for you, at ground level. Humans, bless their hearts, understand that. They try to tolerate all kinds of sniffing, most kinds of snacking, and even, if it's bare ground and the neighbours can't see it, a little digging. They draw the line, however, at mud-munching. But we'll come to that in a minute.

One thing you may like to graze on is grass, in addition to certain weeds. Humans tend to feel uncomfortable about this. They assume that you might be feeling ill, even though you are in fact at the top of your form, in fine fettle and full of the joys of the season. The truth is that you like a little greenery every so often, which may once upon a time have lingered in the gut of some scavenged animal – but you don't find that sort of thing strewn across your kibble. And kibble or stew with a demi-glace reduction are what you are eating these days, not scavenged animals. So to make up for the lack, you snack on grass. It surprises you that humans, who feed on lettuce and water cress, to say nothing of "herbal tea", should be so concerned about your habit. And certainly, there is no reason to give it up, as long as the grass you're browsing is fairly clean and has not just been sprayed with weed killer or pesticide. Mostly you're just flossing your teeth with it, anyway.

Paradise in a pan

Sometimes, this just ain't enough. Not often! But sometimes.

All the same, you may want to keep your inner sheep somewhat under cover: a quick passing snap at some tall juicy blades is less inflammatory than hell-for-leather chomping. Once your human observes that grass-fancying is not a symptom of rabies, lunacy, or athlete's foot, your grazing sessions can be franker and less furtive.

Now we come to a touchier issue, which is mud. However indulgent your human is with grass, I guarantee they'll be alarmed about mud. Mud-munching happens when you've had it with grass, there's some sort of tasty flavour flirting with your lips, and you suddenly feel slightly hungry. Nonetheless, try to fight the temptation. Humans are aghast at mud-munching, imagining that you must be deficient in nutrition, or if not that, then disastrously bored, or if not that, then not of sound mind.

If they catch you doing it – and the sand and soil clinging to your muzzle is sure to alert them – they may alter your diet, and you may not like the new one. They

may decide to monitor you constantly, which could spoil some of your other secret enjoyments. Worst of all, they may take you to the vet, and then you'll be in for weighing, prodding, poking, and being called "Bambi-eyes". Best to admire mud from a distance, don't you think?

Be An Easy Sitter

Sitting is the magic activity. It can only ever help you to get whatever you want. It's the easiest thing in the world. And yet humans are ridiculously impressed by it! Why is this so? What difference does it make whether your posterior is several inches off the ground or positioned right on top of it? The explanation is simple, really. Humans like frolicking, spirited dogs when they're in the distance, but up close they like quiet, demure ones.

In fact, the bigger the dog, the more important it is to be good at sitting. Some dogs can get near human eye-level by rearing up, while others can do the same thing just by standing. But if you want to touch human hearts –

and make them more willing to do something for you –

the best thing is not to stare them down, but rather to gaze up at them. Imagine that your eyes are flowers: they ought to be wide and upturned like day-lilies, not small and droopy like bluebells.

To humans, the sight of you seated is deeply reassuring. It shows you to be alert yet calm, and humans like alertness to be grounded, not flailing and breathing up their necks. Sitting communicates a respect for human control, which paradoxically increases the chances that *you* can influence *them*.

Many dogs unnecessarily complicate their lives, or fail to get all the goodies they have coming to them, just because they refuse to sit when asked nicely (or even when ordered). What is the reason for this self-defeating behaviour? It may be a case of misplaced pride. Often the human is at fault – doesn't give the right hand sign; doesn't mean it; mumbles – but it must also be said that some dogs neglect to apply this most basic of lessons. Perhaps they are just forgetful. Or dense.

You're smarter than this, aren't you?

Don't Be Sick On The Carpet

Now and then, you will ingest things that you really ought to have kept off the menu. It's all right when the non-food items in question are cut bits of thread, the button nose of a rag doll, an unattended tissue, or even a small rubber band. Fact is, you're never going to see those again. And you're not going to suffer: the calorie content is precisely zero, for a start. But what about those times when you get more venturesome: an acorn here, a poison flower there, some nuggets of mulch, or a smattering of owl pellets? Or what if your stomach just doesn't like the dinner *du jour* for some reason? In that case, what once went down will now have to come up, probably at the least convenient moment.

Now here's a little something worth knowing. Humans can accept the fact that now and then you make a mistake in consumption. And when that happens, they will be there with their spatulas, plastic bags, and paper towels, gamely removing the evidence of your embarrassing miscalculation. But – and this is the main point – they would so much rather spatula the tile floor or the wood plank than the Turkish rug they bought on their honeymoon or the modern jobby they acquired from a pricey carpet designer who only makes one-of-a-kind. I know that you can't tell William Morris from Ikea, and that's fine: just tell smooth from fluffy and you'll probably be all right. If you feel the urge to be sick, and there isn't time or opportunity to get outside, try to do the revolting business on a smooth solid surface, just *beyond* the wool shag rug with the sky-high pile. The gratitude of your people for such excellent vomit manners will be profound, and they might even thank you later with some chicken-rice or a poached egg – which you have to admit is a tastier treat than the rabbit droppings you nibbled ill-advisedly.

These self-possessed dogs have gone boating, and I guarantee that their minds are not on grass or on any other dubious snacks.

6.
Humans: Funny Feet, Pitiful Noses,
And A Strange Way of Looking At Things

As we have noted, humans have not yet solved the familiar mystery of the dog. Since your relationship with them involves both love and misunderstanding, you need to develop a sense of when they are right and when they are not.

A prime example is their frankly bizarre ideas about what makes you, the canine, tick. (Tick, as in tock. I know you hate ticks and want nothing to do with them.) They often talk about a "pecking order", as if you were chickens. As if dogs could ever be as simple as that. I mean, look at the diagram:

Do you see yourself in that? No, I didn't think so.

Even their talk about "the pack" leaves something to be desired. Some academic with a fondness for snowshoes and fried mice recipes decides to study wolves, an activity to which you have no objection. The problem is when Dr. Anorak applies the social rules of wolf life to what's going on in *yours*. I mean, really! You'd think that humans would have noticed, in the past twenty thousand years of sharing campfires with you – to say nothing of leg of lamb and flank of mastodon – that your social sensibilities are not the same as a wolf's. All this "alpha" dog stuff went dead as a doornail in the days when dogs developed dewclaws (and no wolf ever has these, unless it's not 100% wolf!), long before humans had huts, hardhats, and handsome houses and *certainly* before the advent of allusive alliteration. Dogs, as long as they have not been raised by wolves or Neanderthals, know how to read human faces, know how to snuggle and how to play the human way (no biting of ears and fingers, etc.). But humans to a wolf are like a full-length mirror: incomprehensible, unrecognizable, and always vaguely threatening.

So humans, despite 20,000 years[1] of assiduously breeding you into a non-wolf, still persist in thinking that there's something wolfy about you. When it comes to *your* subtleties of mind, they still in some ways think like Biff the Caveman did.

There are other more practical incomprehensions, as well. Consider their attitude to barking. Since one bark of yours sounds much like another, they assume that every bark has the same meaning and there's nothing lost if they cut you off. *You* know, of course, that you bark in

---

[1] Truthfully, no one really knows *how* many millennia you've been a dog and not a wolf, for two reasons. One, the early dog looked just like a wolf, and two, barks and howls don't fossilize!

complete sentences. The *sound* is important – gruff, puzzled, inquiring, or outraged – and the duration is significant. There you are, trying to communicate with another dog, and along comes your human, telling you to deep-freeze it. If you were to obey your human at that very instant, your guarding competence and social life would suffer just as quickly.

Other dogs don't like it when you leave them dangling. What is a friendly dog to think when he hears "why don't you..." and you break off before saying "check the pee-mail I left you?"? What sort of dippy watchdog shouts "We don't" and fails to finish with "want any"? I'm not saying, mind you, that you shouldn't honour your human. I'm just saying that you should speak without interruption, and only obey when you're through. As long as you *look* like you're about to stop – turning tail, sitting down, or trotting towards your human – you can usually finish your statement without the human continuing to holler about it.

You just need to be the canine equivalent of the "car in front" at a traffic light: when the foot comes off the brake and the red lights go out, the driver behind feels soothed:  "something's happening!". The driver in front is *awake*, at least. So the driver behind is unlikely to honk with impatience, *even though the front car hasn't moved yet*. Now, I know that you have four paws instead of four wheels, but the principle is the same. Sometimes the *promise of* good behaviour is enough to buy you time to carry on.

On the other hand.... (Humans have two hands, as you may have noticed, which are terrible for walking on but great for doing things like throwing burger buns.) Despite their occasional density, humans can be very astute, and they do at times give helpful warnings. If you have discovered a nest with lots of little things buzzing round it, or a slithery rope with scales all over it, when your human shrieks "leave it!" you certainly should.

Now, what about the human that says, "Spencer, show Miss Prissy-Paws you love her, and give her a kiss"?

Well, that's a different kettle of egg fu yung. On no account should you ever take it seriously.

When your human speaks nonsense like this, momentarily inhabiting the brains of Mary Poppins and Scooby-Doo all at once, you will simply not be there to listen. You will pretend to be suddenly distracted by a fascinating spider/shooting star/letter carrier that you've spotted in the distance. You will rush to the window, perhaps squeaking excitedly or barking. Your human will be distracted, too, and come to see the fascinating object. Where is it? Oh, too bad, it's gone! And by that time, so has Miss Prissy-Paws.

Does this technique sound slightly familiar? Of course it does. It's simply a variation on the temporary-deafness technique discussed in "Walkies Management". Harmless deception and misdirection: that's what training a human is all about.

Which of these dogs is an artless innocent,
and which is a people-beguiling mastermind?
Exactly.
No one can tell. That is the secret of their success.

Bow-Wow (or: the conclusion)

There you have it: the absolutely top-notch, hand-picked saltwater pearls of wisdom that dogs of experience have bestowed on me over the years. Above all, I'd like to give a special thanks to Chummy, my mentor in all things doggy. In fact, she pretty much wrote the book: I'm just a better typist than she is.

If you have not yet learned to decipher letters and a human had to read this to you, I hope that he or she read out faithfully *every* line and didn't skip any compromising bits. Not that skipping would do them any good. If no man is a hero to his valet (or, for want of that, his valet parking attendant), then no human is a lofty sir or madam to the dog. The relationship is too intimate, too full of give-and-take. Even if a human seems godlike at times, *you* know it's really just mummy or daddy making the car move or wafting food into your bowl. You never lose your perspective. But the humans, sitting on their wing-chair cloud in their bathrobe-toga, eating their thousand-calorie ambrosia and wondering where they left their glasses, sometimes try to take their special powers too far. They believe they are the masters of your universe, which of course just makes you want to chuckle. For despite what the training experts told them, your life with them was never going to fit a perfect pattern. And why?

Because dogs have WILLS,

and dogs need THRILLS,

and *comforts*, and a chance to play.

A dog's poem

I've scampered up mountains
And scrambled down stairs;
I've travelled in cars, which are magical lairs;
I've snuggled on pillows
and slept in high chairs:
If only you knew what I know.

Yet what I know best will hardly surprise:
It's only the joy that I see in your eyes;
Your sweet, happy voice,
And your wish to be close,
And I have decided
I love you the most.

Made in United States
North Haven, CT
23 December 2021

13566622R00046